TOM and JERRY ™

This book belongs to:

Name: .... Age: ....

Address: ....

....

CONTENTS

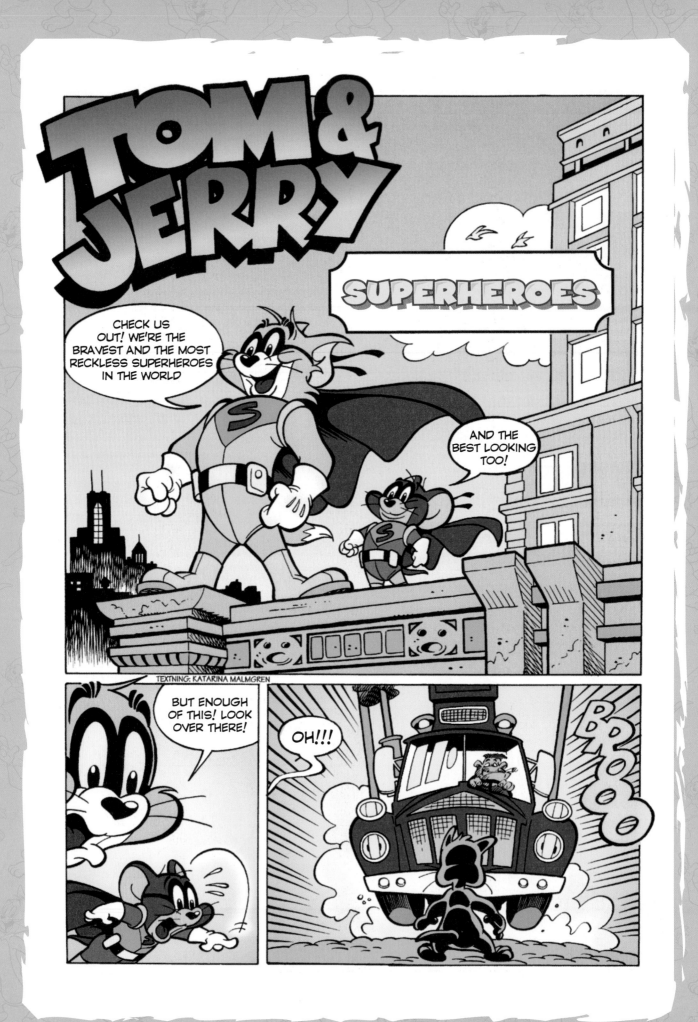

Continued on page 16

13

FRIDGE RAIDERS!

Jerry has raided the fridge and Tom is in hot pursuit. Can you find all the words on the list, hidden in the grid?

T	G	E	J	T	Y	O	Z
O	T	G	E	S	M	B	U
M	M	G	L	K	M	C	S
A	H	S	L	V	B	H	B
T	A	I	Y	Z	Z	E	U
O	M	B	U	T	T	E	R
E	A	X	M	D	J	S	K
S	A	U	S	A	G	E	S

milk ●   cheese ●   tomatoes ●

butter ●   jelly ●   sausages ●

ham ●   eggs ●

Answers on page 61!

14

KING OF THE CASTLE!

Tom and Jerry love playing in the sand. Join the dots to see why Jerry looks so pleased with himself.

Add some colour with your favourite crayons!

15

Continued from page 13

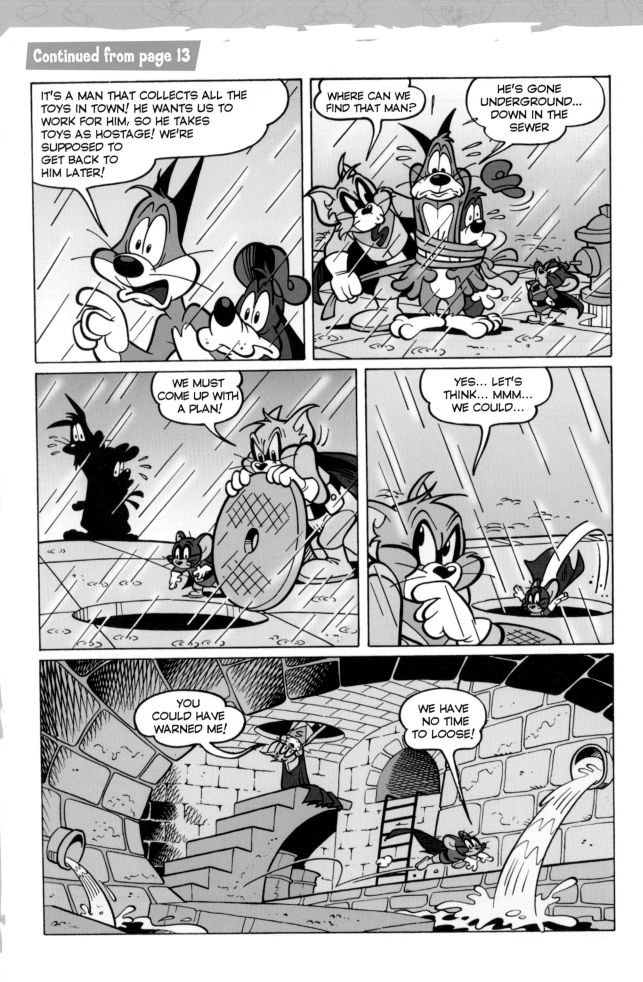

23

Kitchen chaos!

OH NO! Naughty Tom and Jerry have had a food fight in the kitchen! Can you help clean up by ticking the boxes when you find the items?

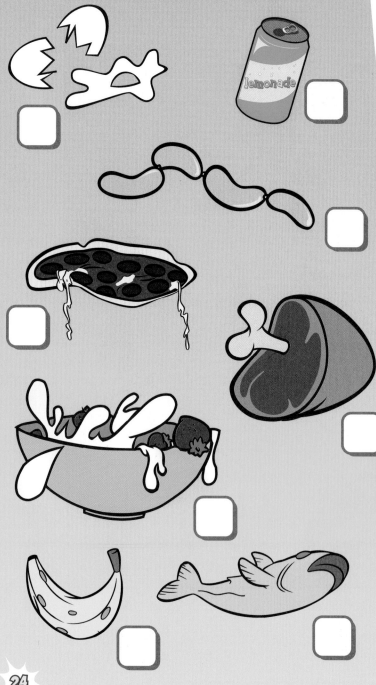

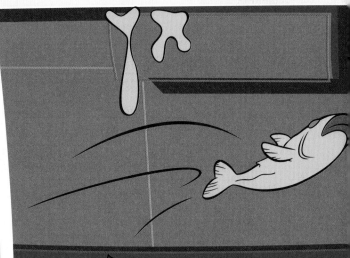

JERRY MONEY-BOX

Turn your pennies into pounds with this cool Jerry money-box! Follow the simple steps to make a brilliant savings bank of your own!

Don't forget... Ask an adult for help!

26

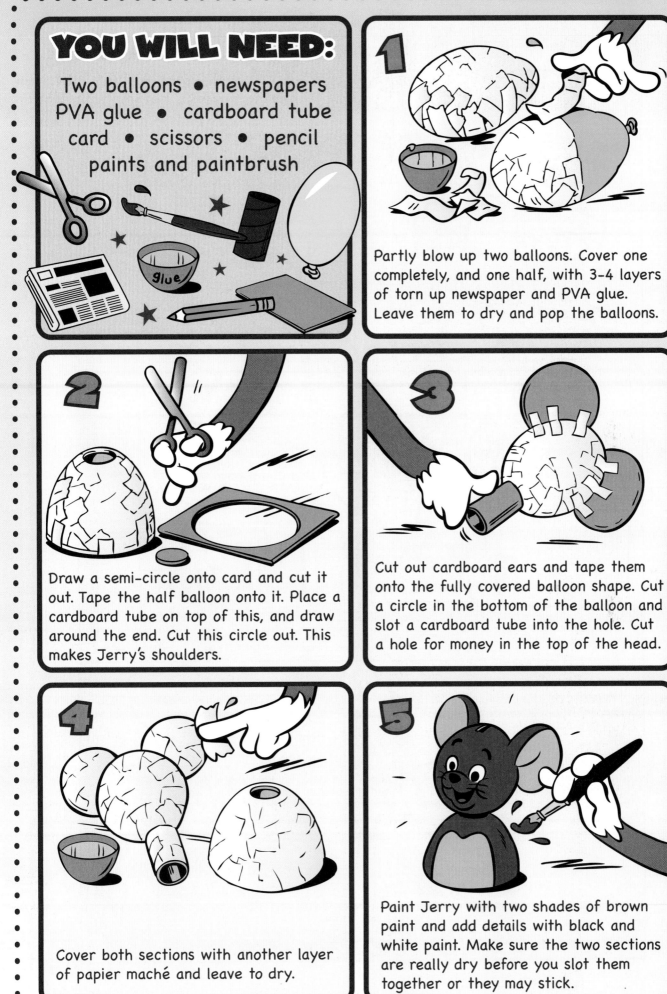

YOU WILL NEED:

Two balloons • newspapers PVA glue • cardboard tube card • scissors • pencil paints and paintbrush

1 Partly blow up two balloons. Cover one completely, and one half, with 3-4 layers of torn up newspaper and PVA glue. Leave them to dry and pop the balloons.

2 Draw a semi-circle onto card and cut it out. Tape the half balloon onto it. Place a cardboard tube on top of this, and draw around the end. Cut this circle out. This makes Jerry's shoulders.

3 Cut out cardboard ears and tape them onto the fully covered balloon shape. Cut a circle in the bottom of the balloon and slot a cardboard tube into the hole. Cut a hole for money in the top of the head.

4 Cover both sections with another layer of papier maché and leave to dry.

5 Paint Jerry with two shades of brown paint and add details with black and white paint. Make sure the two sections are really dry before you slot them together or they may stick.

29

Continued on page 34

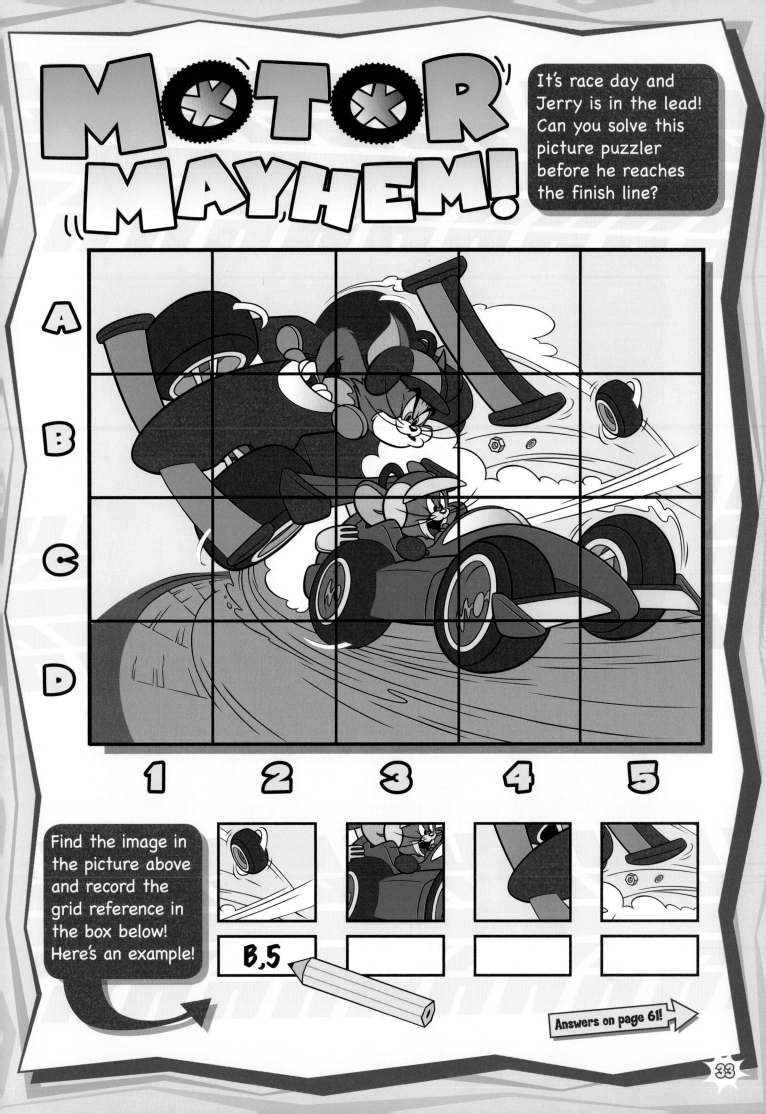

Continued from page 32

MATCHING SHADOWS

The gang are out for some morning exercise. Draw a line to pair up each character with their matching shadow!

1

2

3

6

5

4

9

7

8

Answers on page 61!

39

Chasing cheese!

Help Jerry get back to his mouse hole avoiding the mouse traps. Once you find the correct route, count how many pieces of cheese Jerry collected along the way!

There are _____ pieces of cheese

Answers on page 61!

Making melodies

Tom and Jerry are making music! Can you fit all the musical instruments into the word grid?

piano   trumpet   drum
guitar   triangle   violin

Now you have filled in the grid, use a pencil to match up the words with the correct shadows!

Answers on page 61!

Continued on page 54

Bathtime bubbles!

Can you spot 8 differences between these two pictures?

Answers on page 61!

51

DRAW TOM AND JERRY!

Carefully copy Tom and Jerry square by square.

When you have finished,
add some colour with your
favourite crayons!

Continued from page 50

ANSWERS

Page 14 - Fridge Raiders

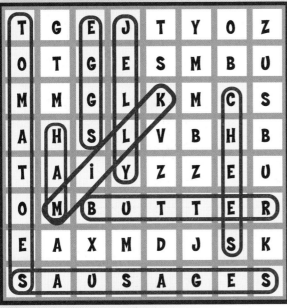

T	G	E	J	T	Y	O	Z
O	T	G	E	S	M	B	U
M	M	G	L	K	M	C	S
A	H	S	L	V	B	H	B
T	A	i	Y	Z	Z	E	U
O	M	B	U	T	T	E	R
E	A	X	M	D	J	S	K
S	A	U	S	A	G	E	S

Page 33 - Motor Mayhem

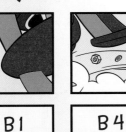

C 3	B 1	B 4

Page 41 - Matching Shadows

Tom: Shadow 5
Spike: Shadow 1
Jerry: Shadow 6

Page 42 - Chasing Cheese

There are 5 pieces of cheese!

Page 43 - Making Melodies

piano

guitar

trumpet

violin

drum

triangle

Page 53 - Bathtime Bubbles